nn as in tennis

A Making words

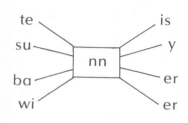 te · su · ba · wi → nn → is · y · er · er

_____
_____
_____
_____

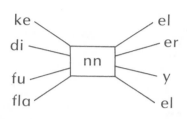 ke · di · fu · fla → nn → el · er · y · el

_____
_____
_____
_____

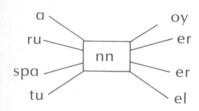 a · ru · spa · tu → nn → oy · er · er · el

_____
_____
_____
_____

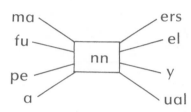 ma · fu · pe · a → nn → ers · el · y · ual

_____
_____
_____
_____

B Choose from the sixteen words you have made. Write the correct word under each picture.

1 _____   2 _____   3 _____   4 _____

C Complete the sentences, using words you have made.

1 A _____ story is one that makes you laugh.

2 Our school was the _____ of the swimming gala.

3 The school sports were held on a warm, _____ day.

4 Trains or cars travel through a _____ to pass through a mountain.

5 Sally has good _____ and is always polite to people.

D Word meanings

1 once a year

2 to tease someone and make them cross

3 main meal of the day

4 shelter for a dog to sleep in

	n	n		
		n	n	
		n	n	
		n	n	

1

pp as in apple

A Making words

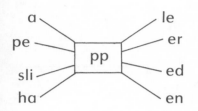

_____
_____
_____
_____

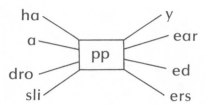

_____
_____
_____
_____

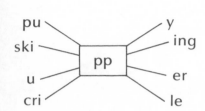

_____
_____
_____
_____

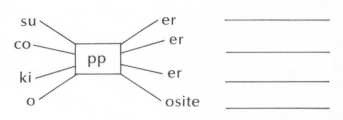

_____
_____
_____
_____

B Choose from the sixteen words you have made. Write the correct word under each picture.

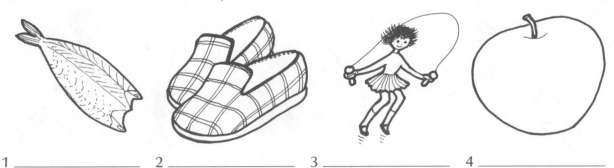

1 _____ 2 _____ 3 _____ 4 _____

C Complete the sentences, using words you have made.

1 Many people put salt and _____ on their food.

2 Pam hurt her ankle when she _____ on the wet floor.

3 Up is the _____ to down.

4 Bill was in pain when he _____ a brick on his foot.

5 Children are _____ when they are playing games.

D Word meanings

1 a young dog

2 opposite of lower

3 last meal of the day

4 person unable to use his body, legs or arms properly

		p	p	
	p	p		
	p	p		
p	p			

rr as in lorry

A Making words

lo, hu, fe, na → rr → y, y, y, ow
_____
_____
_____
_____

che, bu, mi, a → rr → y, ow, or, ive
_____
_____
_____
_____

pa, wo, ca, spa → rr → ot, y, ot, ow
_____
_____
_____
_____

ba, qua, ma, po → rr → ow, y, y, idge
_____
_____
_____
_____

B Choose from the sixteen words you have made. Write the correct word under each picture.

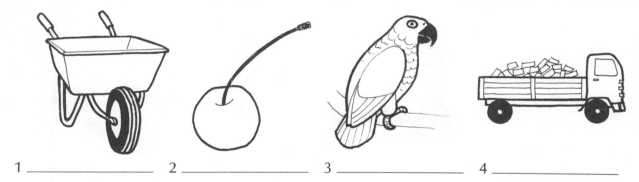

1 _____ 2 _____ 3 _____ 4 _____

C Complete the sentences, using words you have made.

1 The children were late for school so they had to _____.

2 A rabbit makes a _____ in the ground for its home.

3 A garden path is _____ but a street is wide.

4 Dad looks at himself in the _____ while he shaves.

5 My mother is meeting me from the train which will _____ at 6 o'clock.

D Word meanings

1 to feel uneasy or troubled

2 root vegetable, orange in colour

3 breakfast food made from oats

4 to become husband and wife

3

⬛ ss as in kiss

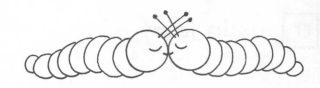

A Making words

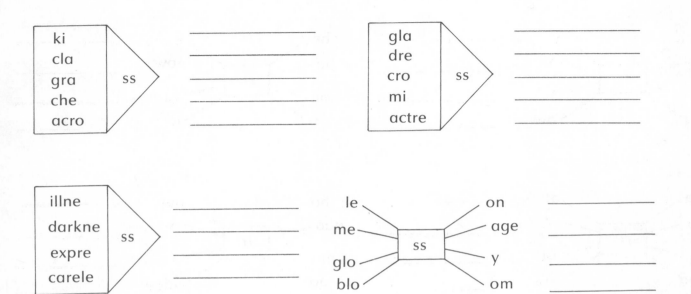

ki
cla
gra
che
acro

ss >

_____
_____
_____
_____
_____

gla
dre
cro
mi
actre

ss >

_____
_____
_____
_____
_____

illne
darkne
expre
carele

ss >

_____
_____
_____
_____

le —
me —
glo —
blo —

ss

— on
— age
— y
— om

_____
_____
_____
_____

B Choose from the eighteen words you have made. Write the correct word under each picture.

1 _____ 2 _____ 3 _____ 4 _____

C Complete the sentences, using words you have made.

1 Look both ways before you walk _____ the road.

2 Betty wore a pretty, white _____ for her party.

3 Stuart made a lot of mistakes in his test because he is _____.

4 The evening sun went down, and _____ fell.

5 Tim's mother gets very _____ when he is naughty.

D Word meanings

1 woman who takes part in a play or film					S	S
2 very fast train					S	S
3 very shiny				S	S	
4 words sent from one person to another		S	S			

4

tt   as in bottle

A   Making words

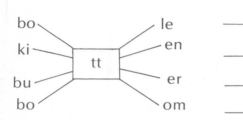

bo — le
ki —
bu — en
bo — tt — er
       om

_____
_____
_____
_____

li — le
a — ic
pre — tt — y
co — on

_____
_____
_____
_____

bu — on
ca — le
gu — tt — er
le — er

_____
_____
_____
_____

ke — le
mu — on
co — tt — age
bu — erfly

_____
_____
_____
_____

B   Choose from the sixteen words you have made. Write the correct word under each picture.

1 _____   2 _____   3 _____   4 _____

C   Complete the sentences, using words you have made.

1   The wrecked ship sank to the _____ of the sea.

2   You can often see a _____ flying in the garden in summertime.

3   When the _____ boiled, I made a cup of tea.

4   The first _____ of the alphabet is 'a'.

5   A dress made of _____ is cool in warm weather.

D   Word meanings

1   opposite of big

2   young cat

3   room just under the roof of a house

4   soft, yellow food made from cream

	t	t	
	t	t	
	t	t	
t	t		

oi as in coil

A Making words

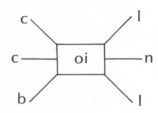

_____
_____
_____

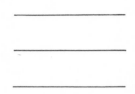

_____
_____
_____

oi + l = _____

oi + ntment = _____

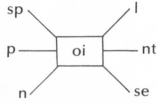

_____
_____
_____

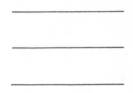

_____
_____
_____
_____

B Choose from the fifteen words you have made. Write the correct word under each picture.

1 _____ 2 _____ 3 _____ 4 _____

C Complete the sentences, using words you have made.

1 It is very rude to _____ your finger at someone.

2 Helen and Jenny would like to _____ the Brownies.

3 The _____ will soothe Ramu's grazed knee.

4 Most milk bottle tops are made from metal _____.

5 Fill the kettle with water and put it on to _____.

D Word meanings

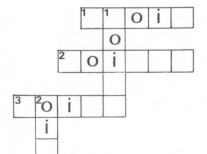

Across

1 to keep out of the way

2 carpenter

3 loud sound

Down

1 you use it when you speak

2 thick liquid from deep underground

oy as in toy

A   Making words

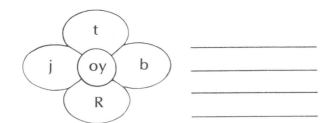

B   Choose from the nine words you have made. Write the correct word under each picture.

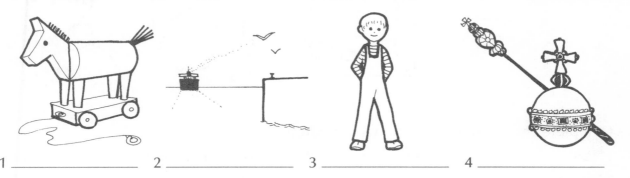

1 _____   2 _____   3 _____   4 _____

C   Complete the sentences, using words you have made.

1   Did you _____ your visit to the circus?

2   Alan and _____ both belong to the Cubs.

3   The new baby brought _____ and happiness to her parents.

4   Buckingham Palace is one of the _____ homes.

5   An earthquake can _____ whole cities.

D   Word meanings

1   to make angry   = _____

2   a journey by ship   = _____

3   child's plaything   = _____

4   male child   = _____

7

ou as in mouse

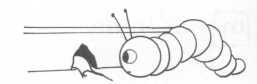

A Making words

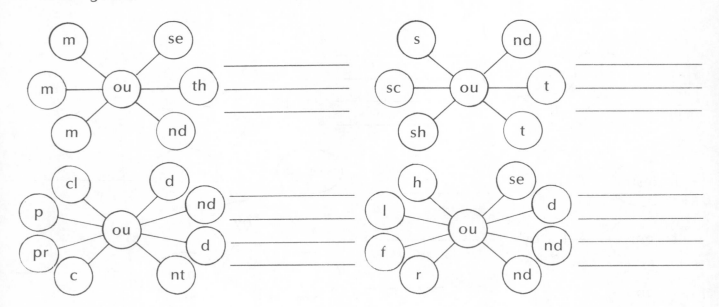

B Choose from the fourteen words you have made. Write the correct word under each picture.

1 _____ 2 _____ 3 _____ 4 _____

C Complete the sentences, using words you have made.

1 The _____ coin is smaller than a fifty pence coin.

2 Philip can _____ up to five hundred.

3 We live in a _____, but Gran lives in a flat.

4 We went on a _____-about at the fair.

5 "I don't want to hear a _____," said the teacher.

D Word meanings

1 to call loudly

2 opposite of humble

3 found in the sky

4 opposite of quiet

5 pile of earth

6 opposite of lost

		o	u	
		o	u	
		o	u	
		o	u	
		o	u	
		o	u	

ow as in town

A Making words

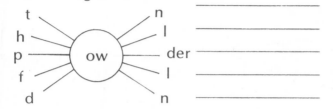

t, h, p, f, d — ow — n, l, der, l, n
_____
_____
_____
_____
_____

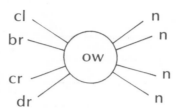

cl, br, cr, dr — ow — n, n, n, n
_____
_____
_____
_____

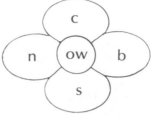

n, c, ow, b, s
_____
_____
_____
_____

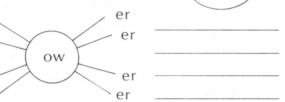

p, t, fl, sh — ow — er, er, er, er
_____
_____
_____
_____

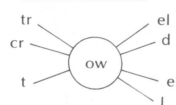

tr, cr, t — ow — el, d, el, l
_____
_____
_____
_____

B Choose from the twenty-one words you have made. Write the correct word under each picture.

1 _____   2 _____   3 _____   4 _____

C Complete the sentences, using words you have made.

1 Sometimes the Queen wears a _____.

2 Mix red, blue and yellow to make _____.

3 A hen is a _____.

4 There was a huge _____ at the football match.

5 The Spanish dancer wore a _____ in her hair.

D Word meanings

Across

2 very large village

3 strength

4 to die in water

Down

1 opposite of up

2 small garden tool

3 spray of water

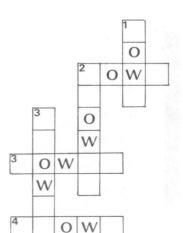

9

$\boxed{\text{oa}}$ as in boat

A Making words

b c g fl → oa → t t t t _____

c f g l → oa → l l l f _____

t l r s → oa → d d d p _____

s cl r t → oa → k k st st _____

B Choose from the sixteen words you have made. Write the correct word under each picture.

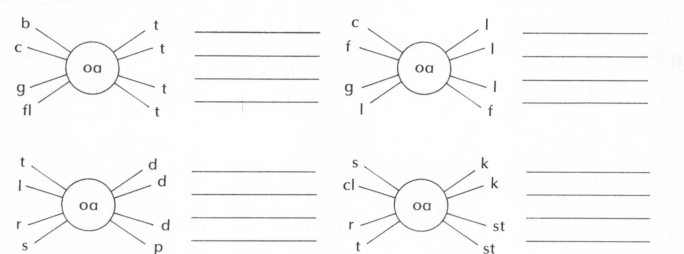

1 _____ 2 _____ 3 _____ 4 _____

C Complete the sentences, using words you have made.

1 We're having _____ chicken for dinner.

2 The camel carried a heavy _____ across the desert.

3 Mum burnt the _____ this morning.

4 Wood will _____ on water, but metal will sink.

5 United won the football match by one _____.

D Word meanings

1 hat and _____

2 young horse

3 Billy and Nanny _____

4 burnt on the fire

5 animal similar to a frog

6 to make very wet

7 between two pavements

ow as in snow

A Making words

sn		_____
sl	+ ow =	_____
sh		_____
fl		_____

cr		_____
gr	+ ow =	_____
bl		_____
kn		_____

l		_____
r	+ ow =	_____
thr		_____
arr		_____

barr		_____
shad	+ ow =	_____
narr		_____
yell		_____

B Choose from the sixteen words you have made. Write the correct word under each picture.

1 _____ 2 _____ 3 _____ 4 _____

C Complete the sentences, using words you have made.

1 Emma wore a brown skirt and a _____ jumper.

2 I _____ where you've been hiding!

3 Come and _____ Gran your new coat.

4 Rashni will _____ the boat across the lake.

5 A _____ builds a nest by itself, but rooks like to build theirs close to each other.

D Word meanings

1 When you _____, you become taller or larger.

2 The opposite of quick is _____.

3 To toss something into the air is to _____ it.

4 The opposite of wide is _____.

5 You might have a _____ when the sun shines on you!

6 The opposite of high is _____.

11

ai as in rain

A Making words

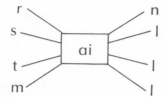

r, s, t, m — ai — n, l, l, l

_____
_____
_____
_____

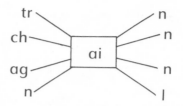

tr, ch, ag, n — ai — n, n, n, l

_____
_____
_____

Word sums

| m | + | ai | + | d | = | _____ |

afr + ai + d = _____

expl + ai + n = _____

p + ai + nt = _____

p + ai + nful = _____

r + ai + lway = _____

s + ai + lor = _____

w + ai + ter = _____

B Choose from the sixteen words you have made. Write the correct word under each picture.

1 _____ 2 _____ 3 _____ 4 _____

C Someone has left two raindrops ◌◌ in place of the 'ai' sound in these words. Can you write the words correctly?

1 r◌◌n _____   2 ag◌◌n _____

3 s◌◌l _____   4 expl◌◌n _____

5 n◌◌l _____   6 s◌◌lor _____

In the box, draw a maid and a sailor catching a train in the rain.

D Word meanings

Across

1 It hurts!

2 works on a ship

3 postmen deliver it

4 most animals have one

5 runs on a railway track

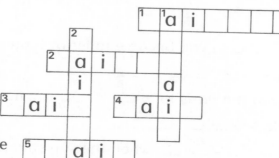

Down

1 to be frightened

2 trains run on this

12

$\boxed{\text{ay}}$ **as in day**

A Making words

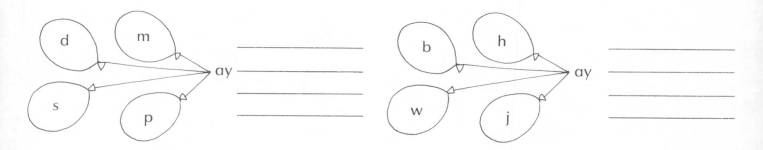

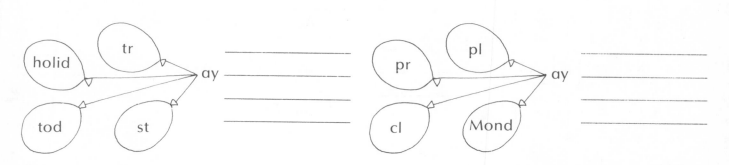

B Choose from the sixteen words you have made. Write the correct word under each picture.

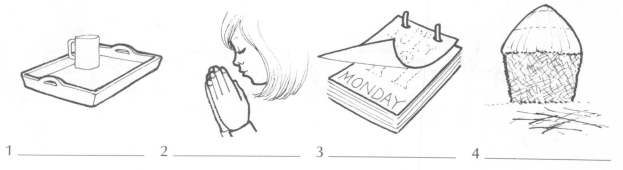

1 _____ 2 _____ 3 _____ 4 _____

C Complete the sentences by choosing the correct words from the brackets.

1 We shall spend our _____ at Smugglers' _____. (Bay, holiday)

2 _____ is Tuesday, but yesterday it was _____. (Monday, Today)

3 Please _____ I go out to _____ now? (play, may)

4 Alex is going to _____ with his gran for the _____. (day, stay)

D Word meanings

     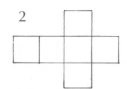

1 *Across:* to speak   2 *Across:* used for modelling   3 *Across:* dried grass
  Down: direction   *Down:* money earned   *Down:* brightly-coloured bird

au as in astronaut

A Making words

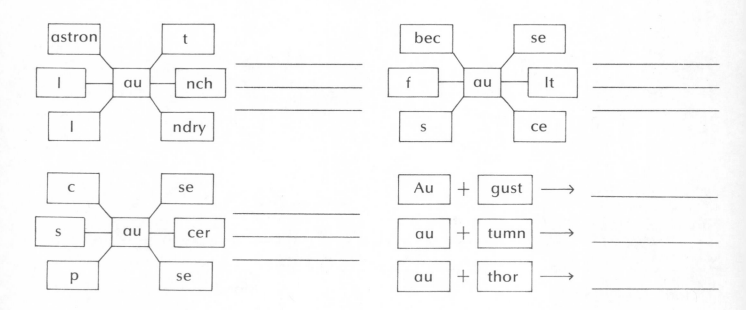

astron		t
l	au	nch
l		ndry

_____
_____
_____

bec		se
f	au	lt
s		ce

_____
_____
_____

c		se
s	au	cer
p		se

_____
_____
_____

Au + gust ⟶ _____

au + tumn ⟶ _____

au + thor ⟶ _____

B Choose from the twelve words you have made. Write the correct word under each picture.

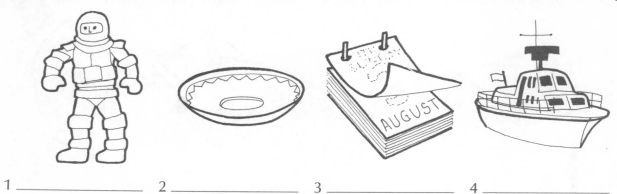

1 _____ 2 _____ 3 _____ 4 _____

C Complete the sentences, using the words you have made.

1 Paul was sent to bed _____ he was naughty.

2 Someone who writes books is called an _____.

3 In _____ leaves turn yellow, red and brown.

4 Sometimes my mother sends sheets and towels to be washed at the _____.

5 The _____ landed safely on the moon.

D Can you sort out these muddled words?

1 lafut

2 eupsa

3 saeuc

4 eusca

	a	u		
	a	u		
	a	u		
	a	u		

14

aw as in paw

A Making words

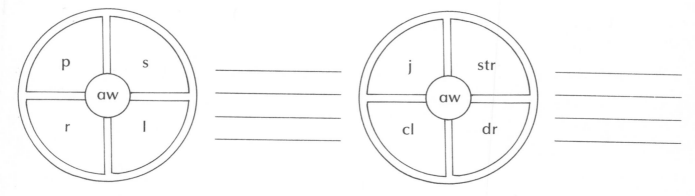

p s r l aw _____ _____ _____

j str cl dr aw _____ _____ _____

Word sums

l + aw + n = _____   d + aw + n = _____

h + aw + k = _____   pr + aw + n = _____

B Choose from the twelve words you have made. Write the correct word under each picture.

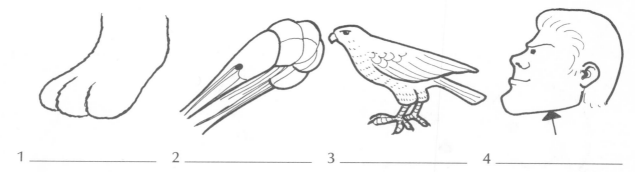

1 _____ 2 _____ 3 _____ 4 _____

C The words in heavy type do not belong. Cross out the wrong word and insert the correct one in each sentence.

1 Lions enjoy eating **straw** _____ meat.

2 The farmer uses **law** _____ for his cows to sleep on.

3 Everyone had to **raw** _____ a picture of themselves.

4 Policemen help to keep **draw** _____ and order.

D Word meanings

1 tool for cutting logs

2 flat piece of grass in a garden

3 A cat may scratch you with one!

4 small shellfish, similar to a shrimp

5 sunrise

6 bird of prey

7 animal's foot

	a	w		
	a	w		
		a	w	
		a	w	
	a	w		
	a	w		
	a	w		

15

sm as in small

A Making words

	all _____		other _____
	art _____		ell _____
sm +	oke = _____	sm +	ack = _____
	ash _____		udge _____
	og _____		eared _____

	ile _____
	ooth _____
sm +	uggler = _____
	oulder _____
	ith _____

B Choose from the fifteen words you have made. Write the correct word under each picture.

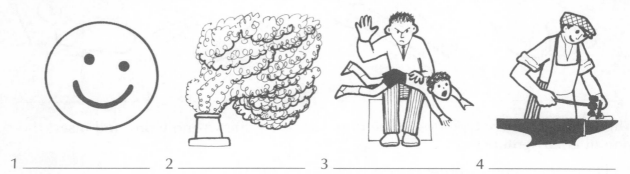

1 _____ 2 _____ 3 _____ 4 _____

C Complete the sentences, using words you have made.

1 A _____ takes things in and out of a country when it is against the law.

2 Janet _____ her face and hands with cold cream.

3 If you drop that egg on the floor it will _____!

4 I can _____ something burning.

5 An elephant is large but a mouse is _____.

D Word meanings

1 to give off smoke but no flame

2 opposite of rough

3 to kill by keeping air from

4 smoky fog in the air

[sn] as in snail

A Making words

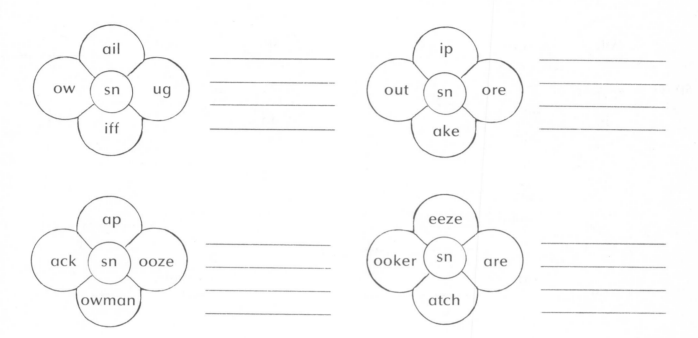

B Choose from the sixteen words you have made. Write the correct word under each picture.

1 _____ 2 _____ 3 _____ 4 _____

C Complete the sentences, using words you have made.

1 A tickling in the nose can cause you to _____.

2 A thief tried to _____ my mother's purse in the shop.

3 The dead twig broke with a _____.

4 We often have falls of _____ in winter.

5 Tony had a _____ of sandwiches and milk.

D Word meanings

1 game played with coloured balls on a special table

2 to make loud breathing noises when asleep

3 cosy, warm and comfortable

4 to take in a quick breath through the nose

s	n				
	s	n			
		s	n		
	s	n			

sp as in spoon

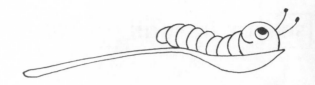

A Making words

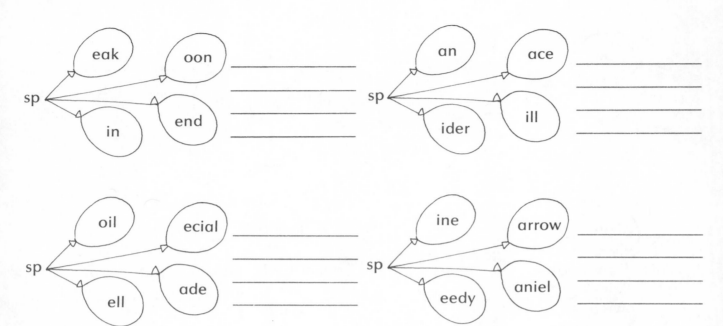

sp — eak, oon, in, end _____

sp — an, ace, ider, ill _____

sp — oil, ecial, ell, ade _____

sp — ine, arrow, eedy, aniel _____

B Choose from the sixteen words you have made. Write the correct word under each picture.

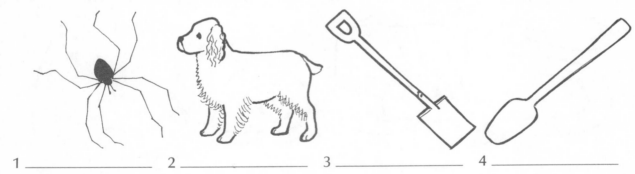

1 _____ 2 _____ 3 _____ 4 _____

C Complete the sentences, using words you have made.

1 I shall _____ all my pocket money on a video game.

2 A dictionary helps you to _____ words you don't know.

3 If it rains this afternoon it will _____ our school sports.

4 The sun, moon and stars are out in _____.

5 A birthday is a _____ day for everyone.

D Word meanings

1 to turn round and round

2 small, brown and grey bird

3 backbone of a person or animal

4 to say something; to talk

			s	p		
s	p					
		s	p			
		s	p			

st as in stamp

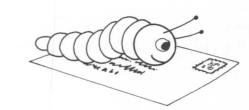

A Making words

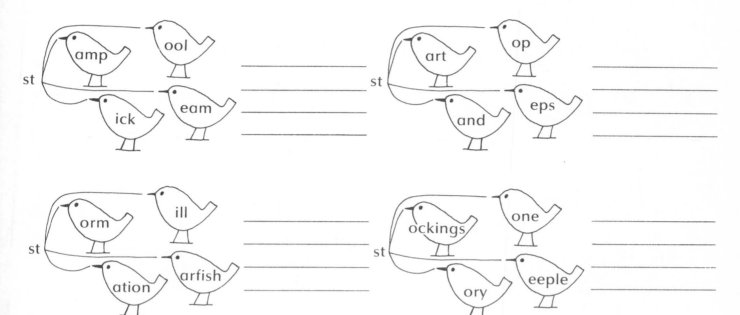

st — amp / ool / ick / eam _____

st — art / op / and / eps _____

st — orm / ill / ation / arfish _____

st — ockings / one / ory / eeple _____

B Choose from the sixteen words you have made. Write the correct word under each picture.

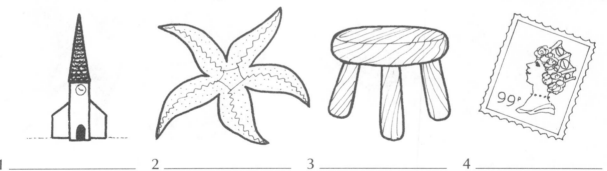

1 _____ 2 _____ 3 _____ 4 _____

C Complete the sentences, using words you have made.

1 Mary wears woollen _____ in the winter.

2 Peter threw a _____ and broke a window.

3 Be careful not to fall down the _____ outside the door.

4 The old man walked with the help of a _____.

5 There were no seats left at the concert so we had to _____.

D Word meanings

1 to begin

2 comes out of a kettle when the water is boiling

3 a true or made-up tale

4 to finish what you are doing

s	t			
s	t			
s	t			
	s	t		

sw as in swim

A Making words

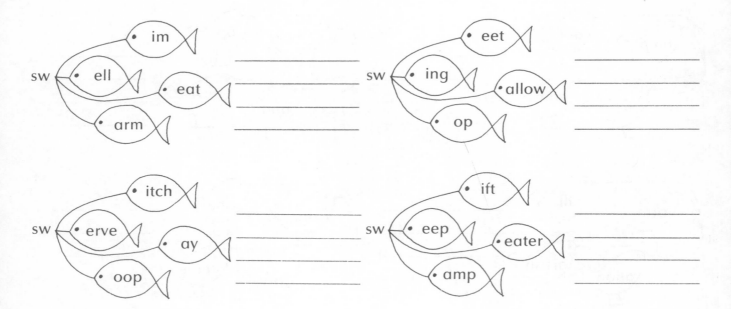

B Choose from the sixteen words you have made. Write the correct word under each picture.

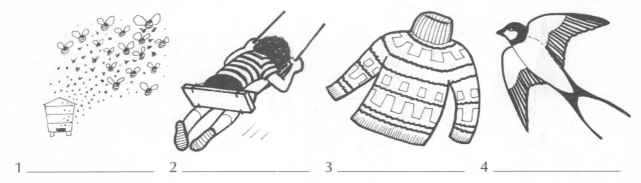

1 _____   2 _____   3 _____   4 _____

C Complete the sentences, using words you have made.

1 We often go to the baths to _____.

2 We _____ when we run and get too warm.

3 Tim helped his dad to _____ up the leaves.

4 Sugar and honey are _____.

5 The car had to _____ to miss the stray dog on the road.

D Word meanings

1 move back and forth or from side to side

2 move swiftly and smoothly downwards

3 a lever for turning electricity on or off

4 to grow larger and fatter

		S	W		
			S	W	
	S	W			
		S	W		

tw as in twig

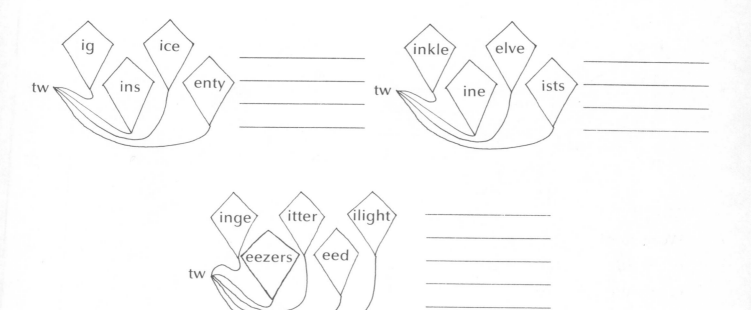

A Making words

tw — ig, ins, ice, enty _____

tw — inkle, ine, elve, ists _____

tw — inge, eezers, itter, eed, ilight _____

B Choose from the thirteen words you have made. Write the correct word under each picture.

1 _____ 2 _____ 3 _____ 4 _____

C Complete the sentences, using the words you have made.

1 The stars _____ in the sky at night.

2 The number between nineteen and twenty-one is _____.

3 Jason felt a _____ in his back after he fell off his bike.

4 The road _____ and turns round the mountain side.

5 The shepherd's warm coat is made from _____.

D Word meanings

1 dim light between sunset and darkness

2 to make small, shrill sounds like a bird

3 two times

4 strong cord or string

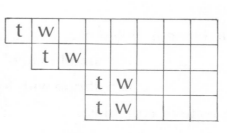

t	w					
	t	w				
			t	w		
		t	w			

21

are as in hare

A Making words

h
r
f   → | are | _____
c   _____
m   _____
                     _____
                     _____

squ
sp   → | are | _____
fl   _____
st   _____
sh   _____
                     _____

Word sums

c + are + ful = _____

c + are + less = _____

B Choose from the twelve words you have made. Write the correct word under each picture.

1 _____   2 _____   3 _____   4 _____

C Complete the sentences, using words you have made.

1 Take great _____ when you cross the road.

2 When we had a puncture we had to put the _____ wheel on the car.

3 "Here's some sweets," said Mum. "_____ them with your friends."

4 The lifeboat men saw an emergency _____ in the sky, and rushed to their lifeboat.

5 It's very rude to _____ at someone.

D What are they?

1 a female horse is called a _____.

2 A _____ is a small animal similar to a rabbit.

3 A _____ is a shape with four equal sides.

4 The opposite of careful is _____.

ore as in core

A Making words

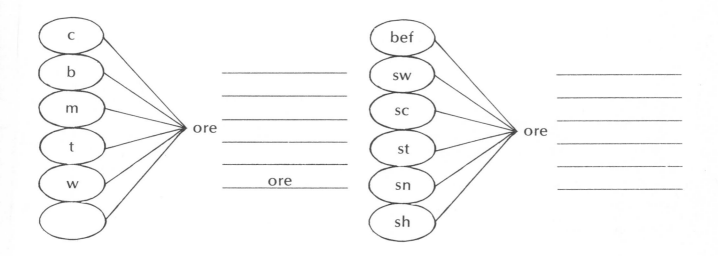

c
b
m
t
w

ore
_____
_____
_____ ore _____
_____
_____ ore _____

bef
sw
sc
st
sn
sh

ore
_____
_____
_____
_____
_____
_____

B Choose from the eleven words you have made. Write the correct word under each picture.

1 _____ 2 _____ 3 _____ 4 _____

C Complete the sentences, using words you have made.

1 Father used a drill to _____ a hole in the wall.

2 David visited a huge iron _____ mine.

3 The _____ of the earth is very, very hot.

4 Oliver Twist asked if he could have some _____ food.

5 Yesterday Lucy _____ her new dress to school.

D Codes

If o = ✱   r = ⋏   e = ₹   decode these words.

1 sc✱⋏₹   = _____   2 sh✱⋏₹   = _____

3 sw✱⋏₹   = _____   4 st✱⋏₹   = _____

5 sn✱⋏₹   = _____   6 bef✱⋏₹   = _____

7 t✱⋏₹   = _____   8 m✱⋏₹   = _____

air as in hair

A Making words

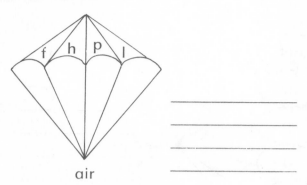

f h p l

air

_____
_____
_____
_____

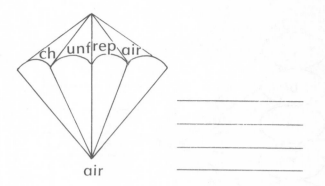

ch unf rep air

air

_____
_____
_____
_____

Word sums

d + air + y = _____

h + air + y = _____

f + air + y = _____

st + air + s = _____

B Choose from the twelve words you have made. Write the correct word under each picture.

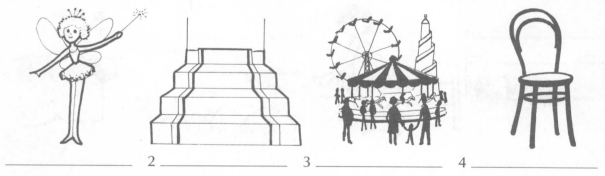

1 _____   2 _____   3 _____   4 _____

C Complete the sentences, using words you have made.

1 Poor Vicki fell all the way down the _____.

2 Bryan had a ride on the Big Dipper at the _____.

3 Perhaps Dad will be able to _____ the broken watch.

4 "I think it's _____," shouted Jill, stamping her foot.

5 The _____ smells very fresh early in the morning.

D What are they?

1 cows are milked here

2 found at the top of the Christmas tree

3 a bear lives in one

4 to be covered in hair

5 two of the same kind

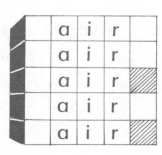

	a	i	r	
	a	i	r	
	a	i	r	▨
	a	i	r	
	a	i	r	▨

Check up oi oy

A Word lists

Learn to spell

oi

boil	ointment	oil
coin	joiner	point
coil	voice	avoid
join	spoil	noise
soil	foil	poison

oy

joy	destroy
toy	enjoy
boy	annoy
Roy	royal
voyage	

B Word search

Hidden in the squares below are eighteen words which contain the letters 'oi' or 'oy'. Search across and down for them and ring them.
Write down the words as you find them. The first one has been done for you.

a	p	o	i	n	t	b	o	y	n	n	c
b	d	e	s	t	r	o	y	o	b	n	o
b	r	c	o	j	o	i	n	e	r	o	i
a	v	o	i	d	y	l	a	f	o	i	l
t	n	i	l	a	e	n	j	o	y	s	j
o	i	n	t	m	e	n	t	n	a	e	o
y	v	o	y	a	g	e	o	i	l	g	y

1 _____point_____   2 _____
3 _____   4 _____
5 _____   6 _____
7 _____   8 _____
9 _____   10 _____
11 _____   12 _____
13 _____   14 _____
15 _____   16 _____
17 _____   18 _____

C Similar and opposite

Write down words with similar meanings to:

1 happiness _____   2 carpenter _____

3 plaything _____

Write down words with opposite meanings to:

4 create _____   5 please _____   6 girl _____

7 leave _____

D Word meanings

1 A _____ is a journey made by sea.

2 A soothing cream is called an _____.

3 When water is heated to 100°C it will _____.

4 Britain obtains a lot of _____ from under the North Sea.

25

Check up   ou   ow

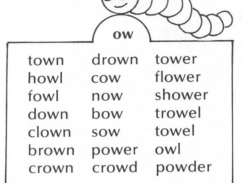

A Word lists

Learn to spell

ou

mouse	pound
mouth	proud
mound	count
sound	house
scout	loud
shout	found
cloud	round

ow

town	drown	tower
howl	cow	flower
fowl	now	shower
down	bow	trowel
clown	sow	towel
brown	power	owl
crown	crowd	powder

B Crossword

Across

1 wise, clever bird

2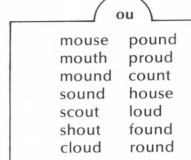

3 female pig

4 opposite of quiet

5 [flower drawing]

6 very large village

7 large gathering of people

8 [shower drawing]

9 $4 + 7 =$

Down

1 carries rain

2 [house drawing]

3 [trowel drawing]

4 to die in water

5 mixture of red and green

6 [tower drawing]

7 [crown drawing]

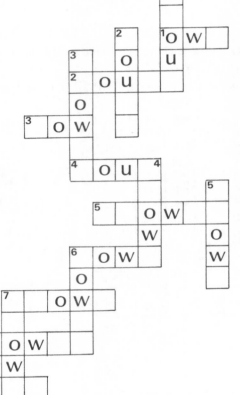

C Opposites and genders

Write down the words with opposite meanings to:

1 whisper _____   2 humble _____   3 lost _____

Write the male or female word in each space:

4 bull _____   5 boar _____   6 Guide _____

D What are they?

1 You might see a _____ at the circus.

2 A _____ is the sound made by a wolf.

3 There are one hundred pence in a _____.

4 A _____ is a small animal which likes to nibble cheese.

Check up [oa ow]

A Word lists

Learn to spell

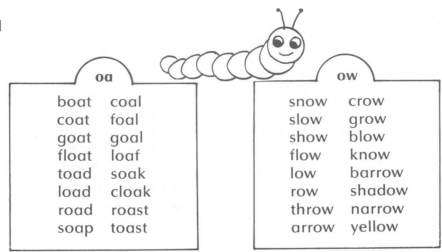

oa	
boat	coal
coat	foal
goat	goal
float	loaf
toad	soak
load	cloak
road	roast
soap	toast

ow	
snow	crow
slow	grow
show	blow
flow	know
low	barrow
row	shadow
throw	narrow
arrow	yellow

B

Hidden in the squares below are seventeen words which contain the letters 'ow' or 'oa'.
Search across and down for them and ring them.
Write down the words as you find them. The first one has been done for you.

b	l	o	w	o	c	s	n	o	w	l	l
i	b	a	r	r	o	w	v	e	r	s	o
l	o	a	d	o	a	s	h	a	d	o	w
c	a	t	r	w	t	o	a	s	t	a	i
o	t	h	r	o	w	u	a	h	o	k	m
k	n	o	w	a	r	m	r	o	a	s	t
a	d	u	y	e	l	l	o	w	d	k	e

1 ___blow___ 2 _____

3 _____ 4 _____

5 _____ 6 _____

7 _____ 8 _____

9 _____ 10 _____

11 _____ 12 _____

13 _____ 14 _____

15 _____ 16 _____

17 _____

C Similar and opposite

Write down words with similar meanings to:

1 street _____ 2 bread _____ 3 young horse _____

Write down words with opposite meanings to:

4 quick _____ 5 wide _____ 6 sink _____

D What are they?

1 A Billy _____ has a beard and horns.

2 Ravens, rooks and jackdaws are all members of the _____ family.

3 A nurse wears a _____ to keep her warm.

4 You can shoot an _____ from a bow.

Check up   ai ay

A Word lists

Learn to spell

ai	
nail	maid
sail	afraid
tail	explain
mail	paint
train	painful
chain	railway
again	sailor
rain	waiter

ay	
way	tray
may	pray
say	clay
pay	play
bay	stay
hay	Monday
day	holiday
jay	today

B Word pyramid

Begin at the top brick, and make your way down to find eleven words.

Pyramid:

```
                M
              o   n
            d  a  y  m
          a  i  l  p  a  i
        n  t  p  r  a  y  c  h
      a  i  n  h  a  y  m  a  i  d
    w  a  i  t  e  r  h  o  l  i  d  a
  y  e  x  p  l  a  i  n  s  a  i  l  o  r
```

1 _____   2 _____

3 _____   4 _____

5 _____   6 _____

7 _____   8 _____

9 _____   10 _____

11 _____

C Similar and opposite

Write down words with similar meanings to:

1 frightened _____   2 wages _____

3 locomotive _____

Write down words with opposite meanings to:

4 night _____   5 painless _____   6 go _____

D What are they?

1 A _____ is a bird with blue and black wings.

2 _____ is water falling in drops from the clouds.

3 A female servant is called a _____.

4 Trains stop for passengers at the _____ station.

5 Grass which is cut, dried and baled is called _____.

28